• HBJ READING PROGRAM •

# SAND CASTLES

 LAUREATE EDITION

## LEVEL 5

Bernice E. Cullinan
Roger C. Farr
W. Dorsey Hammond
Nancy L. Roser
Dorothy S. Strickland

**HBJ** **HARCOURT BRACE JOVANOVICH, PUBLISHERS**
Orlando   San Diego   Chicago   Dallas

## Acknowledgments

For permission to reprint copyrighted material, grateful acknowledgment is made to the following sources:

*David A. Adler and N. M. Bodecker:* Adapted from *A Little at a Time* by David Adler, illustrated by N. M. Bodecker. Text copyright © 1976 by David Adler, illustrations copyright © 1976 by N. M. Bodecker. Published by Random House, Inc.

*Marchette Chute:* "My Teddy Bear" from *Rhymes About Us* by Marchette Chute. Copyright 1974 by Marchette Chute.

*Four Winds Press, an imprint of Macmillan Publishing Company:* Adapted from "A New Friend" in *Margie and Me* by Beverly Wirth. Text copyright © 1983 by Beverly Wirth.

*Harper & Row, Publishers, Inc.:* Complete text, abridged and adapted, and illustrations from *Ottie and the Star* by Laura Jean Allen. Copyright © 1979 by Laura Jean Allen. "Penthouse" from *Out in the Dark and Daylight* by Aileen Fisher. Text copyright © 1980 by Aileen Fisher. Abridged from pp. 1-2 in *Listen, Rabbit* by Aileen Fisher. Copyright © 1964 by Aileen Fisher. Published by Thomas Y. Crowell. Text and illustrations from "The Kite" in *Days With Frog and Toad* by Arnold Lobel. Copyright © 1979 by Arnold Lobel. Complete text, abridged and adapted, and illustrations from "Little Bear and Emily" in *Little Bear's Friend*, written by Else Holmelund Minarik, illustrated by Maurice Sendak. Text copyright © 1960 by Else Holmelund Minarik; pictures copyright © 1960 by Maurice Sendak. Complete text, abridged and adapted, and illustrations from *Owly*, written by Mike Thaler, illustrated by David Wiesner. Text copyright © 1982 by Mike Thaler; illustrations copyright © 1982 by David Wiesner. "Hippo Paints a Picture," abridged and adapted, from *It's Me, Hippo!* by Mike Thaler. Copyright © 1983 by Mike Thaler. Complete text, abridged and adapted, and illustrations from "A Fish Story" (Retitled: "Pelly and Peak") in *Pelly and Peak*, written and illustrated by Sally Wittman. Copyright © 1978 by Sally Christensen Wittman.

*Random House, Inc.:* "Stars" from *The Joan Walsh Anglund Story Book* by Joan Walsh Anglund. Copyright © 1978 by Joan Walsh Anglund.

*Kathy Shaskan, as conservator to Edward W. Field:* From *I Wonder . . . About the Sky* (Titled: "I Wonder") by Enid Field. Copyright © 1973 by Regensteiner Publishing Enterprises, Inc.

*Daniel A. Storm:* Adapted from "The Race Between the Rabbit and the Frog" (Retitled: "The Race") in *Picture Tales from Mexico* by Dan Storm. Published by J. B. Lippincott Company, 1941.

*USDA Forest Service, P.O. Box 2417, Room 1001 RP-E, Washington, DC 20013:* Adapted from the *Smokey Bear Program* (Titled: "Smokey the Bear") by Jane B. Wetham.

## Photographs

Page 2, HBJ Photo/P.C. and Connie Peri; 3(l), Walsh Bellville/Frozen Images; 3(r), D. Cody/FPG; 19, Photri, Inc./Jack Novack; 51, D. Cody/FPG; 52, Ed Cooper; 53, A. & L. Hoglund/H. Armstrong Roberts; 78(l), James Blank/Photophile; 78(r), HBJ Photo; 79(t), HBJ Photo; 79(b), Doug Wechsler; 80(b), J. Christian/Leo deWys, Inc.; 80(t), HBJ Photo; 81(b), HBJ Photo/Rodney Jones; 81(t), Jonathan T. Wright/Bruce Coleman, Inc.; 82(r), HBJ Photo/Rodney Jones; 82(l), Sea World of Florida, Inc.; 93, A. & L. Hoglund/H. Armstrong Roberts; 94, H. Armstrong Roberts; 95(l), H. Armstrong Roberts; 95(r), Mickey Pfleger; 139, Alexander Calder. *The Circus.* (1926 - 31). Mixed media, includes: wire, wood, metal, cloth, paper, leather, string, rubber tubing, corks, buttons, sequins, nuts and bolts and bottle caps. 54 × 94 1/4 × 94 1/4 inches. Collection of Whitney Museum of American Art. Purchase, with funds from a public fundraising campaign in May 1982. One half the funds were contributed by the Robert Wood Johnson Jr. Charitable Trust. Additional major donations were given by The Lauder Foundation; the Robert Lehman Foundation, Inc.; the Howard and Jean Lipman Foundation, Inc.; an anonymous donor; The T.M. Evans Foundation, Inc.; MacAndrews & Forbes Group, Incorporated; the De Witt Wallace Fund; Martin and Agneta Gruss; Anne Phillips; Mr. and Mrs. Laurence S. Rockefeller; the Simon Foundation, Inc.; Marylou Whitney; Bankers Trust Company; Mr. and Mrs. Kenneth N. Dayton; Joel and Anne Ehrenkranz; Irvin and Kenneth Feld; Flora Whitney Miller. More than 500 individuals from 26 states and abroad also contributed to the campaign. 83.36; 140(l), Pedro E. Guerrero; 140(r), Marie Paluan/Art Resource; 141(t), Pedro E. Guerrero; 141(b), Contour Plowing, 1974, Gouache. 29 1/4 × 43 1/8 inches, Collection of Whitney Museum of American Art, Gift of the Artist; 142(l), Robert H. Glaze/Artstreet; 142(r), Inge Morath/Magnum Photos; 145, H. Armstrong Roberts; 146–147, HBJ Photo/Paul Gerding; 158, Breck P. Kent/Imagery.

Contents: Unit 1, 3, D. Cody/FPG; Unit 2, 53, A. & L. Hoglund/H. Armstrong Roberts; Unit 3, 145, H. Armstrong Roberts; Unit 4, 146–147, HBJ Photo/Paul Gerding.

## Illustrators

Laura Jean Allen: 70–74; Cheryl Arnemann: 166–174; Mary Jane Begin: 6–12; Dave Blanchette: 110–114; N.M. Bodecker: 150–156; Jesse Clay: 116–117; Len Ebert: 176–180; Ethel Gold: 43–48, 158–162, 182–185; Katherine Wilson-Heaney: 22–23; Susan Jaekel: 164–165; Arnold Lobel: 186–196; Diana Magnuson: 14–20; Mary McLaren: 200–223; Elizabeth Miles: 118–126; Jan Palmer: 69; Jan Pyk: 128–136; Maurice Sendak: 24–30; John Slobodnik: 66–67, 138; Jerry Smath: 98–106, 108–109; Susan Swan: 76–77; David Wiesner: 56–64, 68; Bernard Wiseman: 32–40, 42; Sally Wittman: 84–90.
Cover: Dan McGowan

# Contents

iii

# Unit 3
# Smiles . . . . . . . . . . . . . . . . . . . . . . 94

Unit 4
# Long Ago ................... 146

# Awards

The authors and illustrators of selections in this book have received the following awards either for their work in this book or for another of their works. The specific award is indicated under the medallion on the opening page of each award-winning selection.

American Institute of Graphic Arts Book Show
American Library Association Notable
   Children's Books
Randolph Caldecott Medal
Randolph Caldecott Honor Award
Children's Book Showcase
Children's Choices
Christopher Award
Garden State Children's Book Award
International Board on Books for Young People Honor List
Lucky Four-Leaf Clover Award
National Council of Teachers of English Award for Excellence
   in Poetry
John Newbery Honor Award
New York Times Best Illustrated Children's Books
   of the Year
University of Southern Mississippi Medallion

# Lost and Found

In "Lost and Found," you will meet people and animals who find friends.

You will read about a little girl who finds a lost dog.

You will read about a little bear who finds a lost girl.

As you read, look for people and animals who are lost and then found.

Look for people and animals who find friends.

**Jamaica's Find** *by Juanita Havill.*
*Houghton.* Jamaica finds a stuffed
dog and a red hat at the park.
When she brings the dog back,
Jamaica meets the dog's owner and
they become friends.

**Beady Bear** *by Don Freeman. Viking.*
Beady Bear reads that bears live in
caves so he leaves home to find one.

**Little Bear's Friend** *by Else Holmelund*
*Minarik. Harper.* In this book, you
can find out more about Little Bear
and Emily.

**A Letter to Amy** *by Ezra Jack Keats.*
*Harper.* What happens to the letter
Peter mails to a special friend?

**I'll Tell You What They Say** *by Anna Grossnickle Hines. Greenwillow.* Andy takes his teddy bear to meet the farm animals. Sam, the dog, comes and saves the bear.

**Beany and Scamp** *by Lisa Bassett. Dodd, Mead.* Beany Bear tries to help his friend Scamp Squirrel find some nuts. They become lost.

**Two Bear Cubs** *by Ann Jonas. Greenwillow.* Two bear cubs walk away from their mother to have fun.

**Don't Worry, I'll Find You** *by Anna Grossnickle Hines. Dutton.* Sarah loses her doll while shopping with Mother.

*A little dog is lost.*
*How does the dog find*
*a new home?*

# A New Friend

*by Beverly Wirth*

I found you at the playground.
You were lost.
You followed me home.
When Mother saw you, she asked
me where I'd found you.

"I found the dog at the
playground," I told her.
"How do you like my new friend?"

Mother said she liked you very
much, but we couldn't keep you.

You had lost your name tag.
We wanted to help you.
Mother and I went to help you
find your home.

"Is this your dog?" I asked some
people.

"No, this is not our dog," they said.

When we got home,
I made a picture of you.

Mother said, "Let's take this
picture to the post office.
Many people will see it there."

So we went to the post office
and put up your picture.
Then Mother helped me put an ad
in the newspaper.
The ad said:

Found: One small brown dog who
is lost and likes to lick a lot.
Call 555-4556.

When Father came home, he
petted you.

He asked me where I'd found you.

"I found the dog at the
playground," I told him.

"How do you like the dog?
Can we keep it?"

Father told me that he liked
you very much, but we couldn't
keep you.

You were not our dog.

Father and I got you some food.
Then you went to sleep by my bed.
I didn't want you to go away.

The next day a woman and a man
came to our house.

The woman had the ad
from the newspaper.

The man had the picture
from the post office.

They said, "This is Margie.
Margie is our dog."

I felt very sad.

Then the man told me,
"We're going away.
    We can't take Margie with us.
    She needs a new home."

    "Would you like to keep her?"
asked the woman.

    I looked at Mother.
Mother looked at me.
"Yes," Mother said.
"We'd like to keep Margie!"

    I hugged you.

"We'll miss Margie," said the man, "but we're glad that she will have a good home."

"We love her very much," the woman said.
"We know you'll love her, too."

"Thank you for Margie!" I said.
"I do love her."
Then I looked at you, and I said, "Margie, you are mine.
Now you're all mine!"

1. How did the dog find a new home?

2. What did the girl and her mother do to try to find the dog's home?

3. How did the owners find their dog?

4. Why do you think Margie has a good home?

5. When did you first begin to know that the girl and her family would find the dog's owners?

6. The girl and her mother were nice to Margie when she was lost. Why did that turn out to be the best thing for them to do?

*In the last story you read,
Margie found a new home.
How does the little bear in
this story find a new home?*

# Smokey the Bear

*by Jane B. Wetham*

A forest ranger came to our school.
She showed us pictures of the forest
and the forest animals.
The forest ranger told us
a true story about a little bear
named Smokey.

Long ago, a little bear was playing in the forest.

He was playing with his animal friends.

Then, the bear stopped playing.

He smelled something.

He looked at his mother.

She smelled something, too.

The mother bear smelled the
smoke from a fire.

She pushed her little bear
to make him run.

Then he ran after his mother.

He saw other animals running, too.

There was so much smoke that the
bear couldn't see his mother.

All he could see was the smoke
and the fire.

The little bear was afraid.

The bear ran and ran.
The ground was very hot.
The little bear burned his paw.
He climbed up into a tree
and waited.

He hoped that the fire would
go away.

The little bear stayed in the tree a long time.

When the fire had stopped, he looked at the burned forest.

He didn't see any green trees.

He didn't see any other animals.

Then he saw a man walking in the forest.

The man was a forest ranger.

The forest ranger helped the bear down from the tree.

When the ranger saw the bear's burned paw, he helped him.

The ranger called the little bear Smokey.

Soon, Smokey had a new home
in a zoo.

A sign was put next to Smokey's
new home.

The sign told about Smokey
and the fire.

When people went to the zoo
to see Smokey, they read the sign.

They wanted to be Smokey's friends.

People wanted to help prevent
forest fires.

The forest ranger told us that we could be Smokey's friends, too.

She said that Smokey's friends help prevent forest fires.

She told us how to prevent other forest fires.

Now we are all friends of Smokey the Bear.

1. How did the bear find a new home?

2. Why does Smokey the Bear's story make people think about preventing forest fires?

3. Name four things Smokey did after he smelled smoke in the forest.

4. Where do you think Smokey liked to live? Tell why.

5. On what page does the forest ranger start telling the story? How do you know?

6. Smokey was put in the zoo. What was the good thing that people would do after seeing Smokey?

# My Teddy Bear

*by Marchette Chute*

A teddy bear is a faithful friend.
You can pick him up at either end.
His fur is the color of breakfast toast,
And he's always there
   when you need him most.

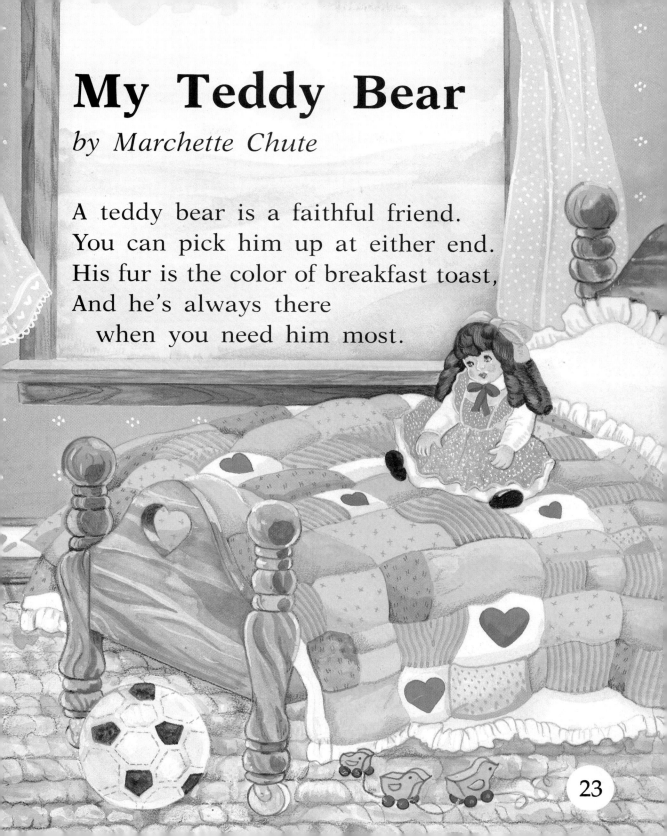

*Smokey the Bear found a new home.*
*What does the bear in this story find?*

# Little Bear and Emily

*by Else Holmelund Minarik*

Little Bear sat in the top of a high tree.

He looked all about him at the wide, wide world.

24

He saw the green hills.
He saw the river.
Far, far away he saw the blue sea.
He saw the tops of trees.
He saw his house.
He saw Mother Bear.

He began to climb down the tree.
On the way down he saw a little
green worm.

"Hello," said the little green worm.
"Talk to me."

"I will talk some other time," said
Little Bear.
"Now I must go home for lunch."

Little Bear climbed all the way
down the tree.
There he saw a little girl.

"I think I am lost," said the
little girl.

"Could you see the river from
the treetop?"

"Oh, yes," said Little Bear.
"I could see the river.
Do you live there?"

"Yes," said the little girl.
"My name is Emily."

"I am Little Bear.
I can take you to the river."

So, Little Bear and Emily walked
and talked together.
Soon they came to the river.

"I see my mother and father,"
said Emily.

"My mother is calling," said
Little Bear.
"I must go home for lunch.
Good-bye, Emily."

"Good-bye, Little Bear.
Come and play with me again."

"I will," said Little Bear.

Little Bear went home.
He hugged Mother Bear and asked,
"Do you know what I just did?"

"What did you just do, Little Bear?"
asked Mother Bear.

"I climbed to the top of a tree,
and I saw the wide world.

I saw the blue sea," said Little Bear.
"And on the way down, I saw a
little green worm.

I climbed all the way down," he said.
"Then what do you think I saw?"

"What did you see?" asked
Mother Bear.

"I saw a little girl named Emily,"
said Little Bear.
"She was lost, so I helped her
to get home.
Now I have a new friend.
Who do you think it is?"

"The little green worm," laughed
Mother Bear.

Little Bear laughed too.
"No," he said, "it is Emily.
Emily and I are friends."

1. What did Little Bear find?

2. Why was it a good thing that Little Bear was in the top of a tree?

3. What did you like best about this story?

4. How did Emily find her way home?

5. What makes you think Little Bear and his mother have fun together?

6. How did Little Bear find a friend?

Children's Choices Author

*Someone has sent letters but didn't sign them.*
*Read to find out who sent the letters.*

# The Surprise Letters

*story and pictures by Bernard Wiseman*

"Eddie, here is a letter for you,"
his mother said.

"Who is it from?" asked Eddie.

"Open it and see," she said.

"It must be from one of my best
friends," said Eddie, as he opened
his letter.

"This is funny!" Eddie laughed.
"I have read this letter, but I still don't know who sent it!"

"Isn't there a name on it?" his mother asked.

"The letter isn't signed, but someone drew a funny face on it!" said Eddie.
"I'll read the letter to you."

"Nina has an *i* in her name," said Eddie's mother.

"Linda and Tim have an *i* in their names, too," said Eddie.

"So do Rick and Kim!" his mother said.

"All my best friends have an *i* in their names," said Eddie.
"I'll find out who sent this letter!
I'm going to see my friends now."

Eddie rode his bike to Nina's house.

His friends were there, playing.

"Who sent me a letter and didn't sign it?" asked Eddie.

"Oh," said Tim, "you got
one, too!
We all thought that you were
the one who sent letters to us!
We thought you were the one who
drew the funny faces on our letters."

"I rode my bike over here to find
out who sent my letter," said Linda.
"I thought Eddie did it.
Now I still don't know who
sent it."

"I'll find out who did it,"
thought Eddie.

Eddie said, "Tim, show us
your letter."
Tim showed his letter.

"Linda, show us your letter,"
said Eddie.
Linda showed her letter.

"Kim, show us your letter,"
said Eddie.

Kim didn't have a letter to show.
She just looked down at the grass
and smiled.

"You didn't get a letter, did you?
Are you the one who sent all the
letters?" asked Eddie.

"Yes, I'm the one," said Kim.
"I thought I would surprise you."

"You did surprise us, Kim.
Now we all know who sent the
letters," laughed Eddie.
"You are funny, Kim!"

Kim laughed.
All her friends laughed, too.

1. Who sent the letters but didn't sign them?

2. What clue did Eddie have in his letter?

3. Why did Kim send the letters?

4. How did Eddie find out who sent the letters?

5. When did you first begin to know that Kim sent the letters?

6. Kim surprised her friends. How do you know that they liked Kim's surprise?

# Maps

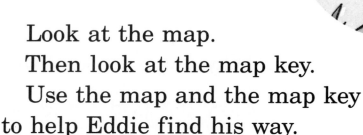

Look at the map.
Then look at the map key.
Use the map and the map key
to help Eddie find his way.

1. Eddie is at home.
   Tell him how to get to school.

2. Eddie is at school.
   Tell him how to get to the
   playground.

3. Eddie is on the playground.
   Tell him how to get to Nina's
   house.

4. Eddie is at Nina's house.
   Tell him how to get to the
   post office.

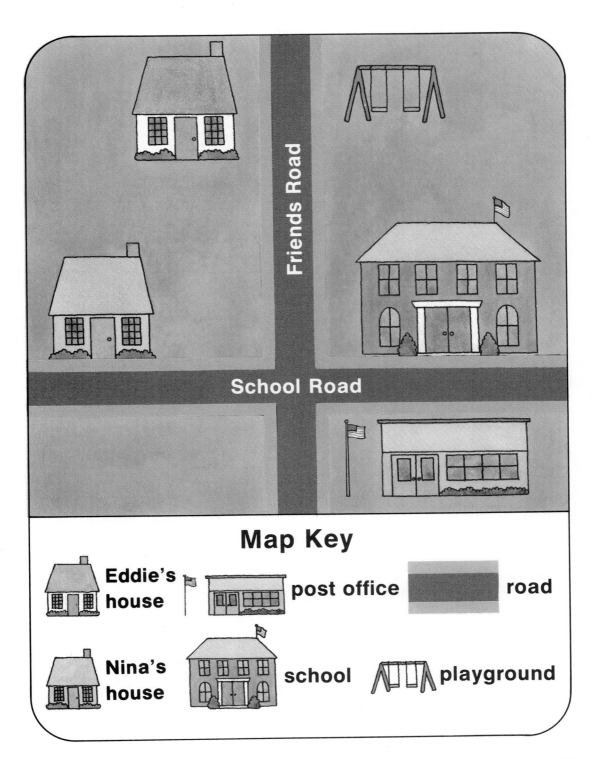

Friends Road

School Road

## Map Key

Eddie's house

post office

road

Nina's house

school

playground

43

*Amy mails a letter to
her grandma and grandpa.
Read to find out how Amy's
letter gets to their house.*

# Amy Mails a Letter

*by Ann Becker*

Amy sent a letter to
her grandma and grandpa.
　　She put her letter into a mailbox.
　　Soon a mail carrier took the mail
from the mailbox to a post office.

The mail was first sorted by size.
Then it was sorted by ZIP code.
The ZIP code told where the letters
were to go.

Next, a truck took Amy's letter
to an airplane.
   The mail was put on the airplane.
   The airplane flew to another town.

The mail then went from the airplane to a big post office.

The mail was sorted again by size and by ZIP code.

Then a truck took Amy's letter to a little post office.

A mail carrier took Amy's letter to her grandma and grandpa's house.

They were very happy to get the letter from Amy.

Then they sent a letter to Amy.

How did the letter get to Amy?

**Discuss the Selection**

1. How did Amy's letter get to her grandma and grandpa's house?

2. How many ways is a letter sorted?

3. How is a letter moved from one place to another?

4. Why do you think Grandma and Grandpa were happy to get Amy's letter?

5. What helped you to follow the way Amy's letter got to her grandma and grandpa's house?

6. To how many post offices did Amy's letter go?

49

# Thinking About "Lost and Found"

You have read about people and animals who were lost and found.

Many of the people in these stories found new friends.

Little Bear helped Emily find her way home.

He found a new friend, too.

How is helping others a good way to find new friends?

What did Eddie and his friends find?

As you read the stories in this book, look to see how friends help each other.

Look for people and animals who find out about new things, too.

1. In the stories that you read, who were lost or found?

2. How are Eddie and the girl who found Margie the same?
How are they not the same?

3. What did Amy and Kim do that was the same?
What did they do that was not the same?

4. Is "Lost and Found" a good name for this unit? Why?

# Land and Sea

There are many things to know about the land and the sea.

There are many things to know about our world.

In the stories in "Land and Sea," people and animals try to learn more about the world.

They learn many things about each other, too.

As you read, look for the things that the people and animals learn about each other and the world.

Look for things that you can learn, too!

**A Fish Out of Water** *by Helen Palmer. Random House.* A boy finds out that he fed his fish too much.

**Keep Running, Allen!** *by Clyde Robert Bulla. Crowell.* Allen is tired of trying to keep up with his older brothers and sister.

**I Wish I Could Fly** *by Ron Maris. Greenwillow.* Turtle wishes he could be like other animals until his shell protects him during the rain.

**Sand Dollar, Sand Dollar** *by Joyce Audy Dos Santos. Lippincott.* A boy wishes the sea would go away so he could play in the sand. Then he thinks of the sea animals.

**Owliver** *by Robert Kraus. Dutton.* Owliver doesn't know what he should be when he grows up.

**More Tales of Oliver Pig** *by Jean Van Leeuwen. Dial.* The story "Questions" is one of the four stories about Oliver Pig in this book.

**Peterkin Meets a Star** *by Emilie Boon. Random House.* What happens when a boy pulls a star out of the sky and takes it home?

**The Sky Is Full of Stars** *by Franklyn M. Branley. Harper.* This book tells how to find special stars and star pictures in the sky.

*Owly wants to know many things about the world. Read to find out what Owly asks his mother.*

# Owly

*by Mike Thaler*

Owly started asking questions when he was two.

He would sit all night with his mother and look at the stars.

"How many stars are in the sky?" he asked one night.

"Many," said his mother.

"How many?" asked Owly, looking up.

"Count them," she said.

56

"One, two, three, four, . . ." counted Owly.

The next morning Owly was still counting.

"How many stars are in the sky?" asked his mother.

"More than I can count," said Owly, closing his eyes.

The next night Owly looked up at the sky again.

"How high is the sky?" he asked his mother.

"Very high," she said, looking up.

"How high?" asked Owly.

"Go and see," said his mother.

Owly flew up into the sky.
He flew as high as he could fly.

In the morning his mother asked,
"How high is the sky?"

"Higher than I can fly," said Owly,
closing his eyes.

The next night Owly looked at the waves in the sea.

"How many waves are there in the sea?" he asked his mother.

"Many waves," she said.

"How many?" asked Owly.

"Go and count them," she said.

So Owly flew to the sea and counted the waves.

"One, two, three, four, . . ." counted Owly.

In the morning Owly saw that there were still many more waves in the sea. He flew back to his mother.

"How many waves are in the sea?" she asked.

"More than I can count," said Owly, closing his eyes.

The next night Owly asked his mother, "How deep is the sea?"

"Very deep," she said.

"How deep?" asked Owly.

His mother looked up at the sky.
"It is as deep as the sky is high," she said.

Owly looked up.
He sat there all night thinking about the sky, and the stars, and the waves, and the sea.
He thought about all his mother had told him.

In the morning Owly turned to his mother and said, "I love you."

"How much?" asked his mother.

"Very much," said Owly.

"How much?" she asked.

Owly gave her a hug.
"I love you as much as the sky is high and the sea is deep," Owly said.

Owly's mother gave him a hug.
"Do you have any more hugs to give me?" asked Owly.

"Many more," she said as she hugged him again.

"How many more?" asked Owly as he went to sleep.

"As many hugs as there are waves in the sea and stars in the sky," said his mother.
And she did.

1. Name some things that Owly asked his mother.

2. How do Owly and his mother feel about each other? How do you know?

3. What did Mother keep telling Owly when he asked questions?

4. Were the answers Owly's mother gave him good one's? Why?

5. When did you know that Owly was not going to find out how deep the sea is?

6. The waves in the sea and the stars in the sky were too many to count. What is another thing that Owly couldn't count?

# I Wonder

*by Enid Field*

I wonder if somebody knows
where the big sky really goes;
where it starts and where it ends,
and if the earth and sky are friends?

I wonder how the sun can play
the morning trick it does each day,
making day come out of night,
changing dark to yellow light?

I wonder why I like to lie
in my bed and watch the sky
and feel its darkness gently creep
around me as I go to sleep?

# Predict Outcomes

**1.** Look at the picture.
What do you think will happen next?
How do you know?

Now read the sentences to see if you were right.

Owly is asking a question.
He wants to know how many raindrops are in the sky.
Owly will count the raindrops.

Were you right about the picture?
Why or why not?

2. Look at the picture of the boat.
   What do you think will happen next?
   How do you know?

Now read the sentences to see if
you were right.

The man is on a boat.
He is near the side of the boat.
He will go into the water to swim.

Were you right about the picture?
Why or why not?

*Ottie jumped into the sea to find a star.*
*What does she learn about the stars?*

# Ottie and the Star

*story and pictures by Laura Jean Allen*

Ottie and her mother
lived by the sea.
Ottie loved to sit by the sea
at night and look up at the stars.

One night Ottie thought,
"I want to get a star!
I wish they were not so far away."
Ottie looked at the stars in
the water.
"Those stars are not too far away,"
she thought.
"I think I'll get one."

Ottie jumped into the water.

She swam down, down, down, looking for a star.

She saw something near a rock.

"A star!" Ottie shouted.

She swam over to get it.

It was a shark!

The shark wanted to get Ottie.

Ottie swam away as fast as she could.

Just in time, Ottie saw a cave.

She swam into it.

Ottie waited in the cave a long time.

Then she looked outside.

"Hello," said a dolphin.

"I just got away from a shark!"
Ottie said.

"Come with me," said the dolphin.
Ottie and the dolphin swam over
and under and up and down.
Then, Ottie saw a star.

"I have to get off now!" Ottie said.
"Good-bye and thank you, Dolphin."

"Good-bye," said the dolphin.

Ottie swam down and got the star.
"Let go of me!" shouted the star.

Ottie wanted to show the star to her mother.

Ottie took the star up to the top of the water.

"Look, Mother! I found a star!" said Ottie.

"That is not a star, Ottie," said her mother.
"It's a starfish."

"It looks like a star," said Ottie.

"I know," said her mother, "but stars are up in the sky.
Starfish live down under the water."

"I want to go home!" said the starfish.

"I'll take you home," said Ottie.

"I know my way home," said the starfish.

Ottie put the starfish back into the water.

"Good-bye, Starfish," said Ottie.

"Good-bye, Ottie," called the starfish.

Ottie and her mother waved as the starfish swam down under the water.

1. What did Ottie learn about stars?

2. Name four things that Ottie did after she jumped into the water.

3. How did you feel when Ottie took the starfish from its home?

4. What did Ottie do to make the starfish happy?

5. How do you know that this is not a true story?

6. What did Ottie need to know before she jumped into the water to find a star?

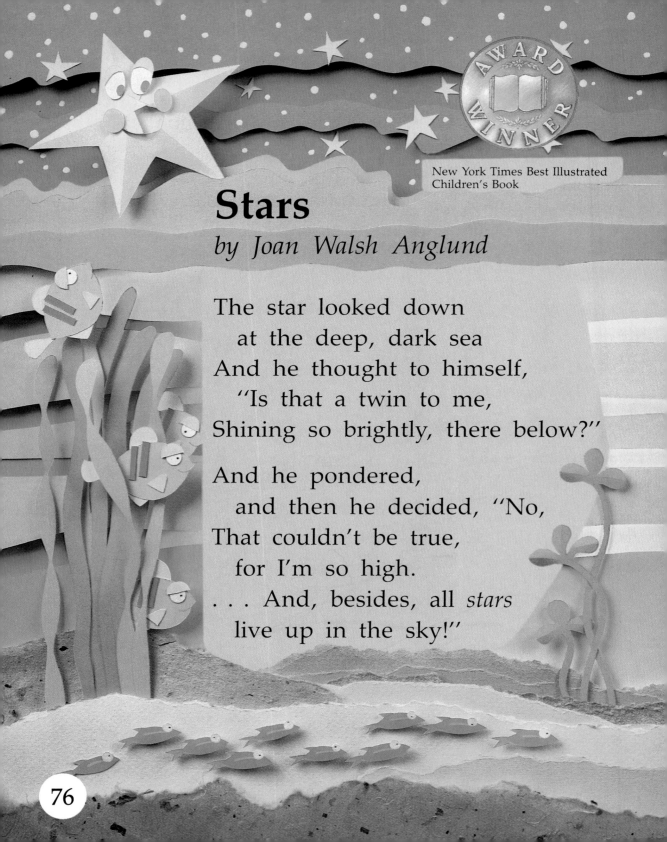

# Stars

*by Joan Walsh Anglund*

The star looked down
   at the deep, dark sea
And he thought to himself,
   "Is that a twin to me,
Shining so brightly, there below?"

And he pondered,
   and then he decided, "No,
That couldn't be true,
   for I'm so high.
. . . And, besides, all *stars*
   live up in the sky!"

And the starfish, below,
    looked up to the sky.
"Why, that's a brother of mine,
    pinned up so high!"
But then he thought,
    "How could that be,

For everyone knows
    *stars* live in the sea!"
So both stars fell asleep,
    each in his blue,
And neither one questioned
    . . . so neither one knew!

*Many people work at a marine park.*
*Read to find out what their jobs are.*

# At a Marine Park

*by Carl Donneley*

If you went to a marine park, you could see many sea animals. You could see starfish, sharks, dolphins, and otters.

Many people work at a marine park. The animals must be fed. Their homes must be cleaned. Some of the marine park animals must be trained for shows.

This is Margie.

Her job is to feed the starfish.

Margie feeds plants and little fish to the starfish.

Starfish don't eat the same way that people eat.

People put food into their mouths.

A starfish pushes its stomach outside its mouth.

It puts its stomach over its food.

Then the starfish eats the food with its stomach.

Here is Robert.

He takes care of the sharks.

One of his jobs is to clean the shark tank.

First a net is dropped into the water.

The net keeps the sharks on one side of the tank.

Then Robert jumps into the water on the other side.

Next he cleans that side of the tank.

Here are Tim and Rita.

Tim and Rita train the dolphins.

They teach the dolphins to do many things.

The dolphins learn to jump out of the water.

The dolphins learn to come when they are called.

They learn to play ball.

Tim and Rita learn how to ride on the backs of the dolphins.

This is Nina.
She trains the otters.
It takes a long time to train the otters.
The otters learn to play ball.
They learn to clap.

Nina, Tim, and Rita like training sea animals.
Margie and Robert like their jobs, too.
Someday, you may want to work at a marine park, too.

1. What are some of the things people who work at a marine park do?

2. How does a starfish eat?

3. How do people and animals learn at a marine park?

4. What marine park animal do you like best? Why?

5. How do you know that this is a true story?

6. Why are people needed at a marine park?

*Peak the peacock can do
something very well on land.
Pelly the pelican can do
something very well in the sea.
What can these two birds
do?*

# Pelly and Peak

*story and pictures by Sally Wittman*

Pelly and Peak were by the sea.
"What a fine day it is!" said Peak.
"I feel like opening my fan!
Close your eyes, Pelly."

Pelly closed his eyes.
"Now open your eyes," said Peak.

"You look like a rainbow!"
said Pelly.

"It was nothing," said Peak.
"All peacocks look like this."

"I wish that I looked like a peacock," said Pelly, "but pelicans are not so fancy."

"Don't be sad," said Peak. "I'll find a way to cheer you up."

Peak sat on a log to think.
"I know," said Peak.
"We can go fishing!"

"Good!" said Pelly.
Pelly went into the water.
He began to swim.

"You forgot your fishing pole,"
called Peak.

"I never use one," said Pelly.

"Be careful," called Peak.
"The water is deep."

"Yes, the water is deep,
but I can swim very well.
Are you coming in?" called Pelly.

"No, thank you," said Peak.
"I never swim.
I will fish from the land."

Peak put a worm on his hook.
Then he dropped the hook into
the water.
He waited for a fish to bite.

The sun was so hot that Peak
went to sleep.

A fish began to eat Peak's worm.

The fish pulled on the pole.

Then the fish swam away
with the worm and the hook
and the pole.

This woke Peak up.

"Come back with my pole,"
Peak shouted to the fish.

Then Peak saw Pelly coming out of the water.

"A fish took my pole!" Peak cried.

"Did you get a fish?"

Pelly opened his bill.
He dropped some fish on the sand.

"Good work!" said Peak.

"It was nothing," said Pelly.
"Fishing is easy for a pelican."

"You see," said Peak, "we are both good at some things."

"Yes, and we are not so good at others," laughed Pelly.

Pelly and Peak went home. They both felt good inside.

90

1. What could Pelly do? What could Peak do?

2. How did Pelly feel when Peak opened his tail?

3. How did Peak learn what Pelly could do?

4. What did you like best about Pelly? What did you like best about Peak?

5. What did you read that made you think that Pelly and Peak were good friends?

6. What did Pelly and Peak learn?

# Thinking About
# "Land and Sea"

In "Land and Sea," you met people and animals who learned more about the world and about each other.

Owly asked questions about the stars, the sky, and the sea.

Ottie found out about stars and starfish.

Pelly and Peak learned something very special about each other.

What did the people and animals learn at a marine park?

What did you learn about the world from reading "Land and Sea"?

What questions do you still have?

1. What were some things in the stories that happened on land?

2. What were some things that happened near the sea?

3. How did Pelly, Peak, and Owly find out that they were special?

4. Who in the stories learned something? What did they learn?

5. Why do you think the name of this unit is "Land and Sea"?

# Smiles

It feels good to smile.

It feels good to make others smile, too.

In "Smiles," you will read about friends who help each other.

You will read about friends who play funny tricks on each other.

As you read, look for things that make the people and animals in the stories smile.

Look for things that make you smile, too!

**No Good in Art** *by Miriam Cohen. Greenwillow.* Jim finds out he is not really a bad artist when the new art teacher talks to him about it.

**Oliver** *by Syd Hoff. Harper.* Oliver, the elephant, tries to join the circus. His new friends help him get his wish.

**Who's in Rabbit's House? A Masai Tale** *by Verna Aardema. Dial.* Someone is in Rabbit's house and won't let her in!

**Herman the Helper** *by Robert Kraus. Windmill.* Herman, the octopus, spends all day helping others.

**William and Boomer** *by Lindsay Barrett George. Greenwillow.* William finds a lost baby goose. By the end of the summer they are swimming together.

**Lorenzo** *by David McPhail. Doubleday.* An artist finds a home in a forest and makes friends with the animals.

**Helping Out** *by George Ancona. Clarion.* Pictures show children and grown-ups working at jobs together.

**Two Bunnykins Out to Tea** *by Warrener. Viking.* Bunting and Babs Bunnykins fight over a toy, but Grandmother helps them.

*Mama Fig is not happy in her house on the hill. How do Mr. Fig and his friends make her happy?*

# Mama Fig's House

*by Elizabeth K. Cooper*

These are people who are needed for the play.

| | | |
|---|---|---|
| **Narrator** | **Mr. Fig** | **Rabbit** |
| **Owl** | **Mama Fig** | **Mouse** |
| **Turtle** | **Red Hen** | |

**Narrator:** Mr. Fig and his friends
are going to see Mama Fig.
Their laughter is heard as they fly
higher and higher in the Figmobile.

**Owl:** Oh, Mr. Fig, I like to ride
in your Figmobile.
It's so much fun!

**Turtle:** Look! It's starting to rain.
When will we get to
Mama Fig's house?

**Mr. Fig:** There it is now.
Keep your magic hats
on, everyone.
The magic hats will help us land
the Figmobile.

**Narrator:** The Figmobile lands
at the top of a hill.

**Mama Fig:** Hello, Son!
I heard laughter.
So I came out to see
who was laughing.
I'm so glad to see you.
How is everyone?
Come in before you all get wet.

**Narrator:** Mr. Fig and the animals
go into Mama Fig's house.
All but Rabbit take their hats
into the house.

**Red Hen:** I'm glad we're inside your
house, Mama Fig.
It's raining so hard!

**Rabbit:** Do you like living
on top of this hill, Mama Fig?

**Mama Fig:** I *should* like it here,
but I don't.
All my friends live at the bottom
of the hill.

**Red Hen:** Perhaps we can help you
find a new house.

**Mama Fig:** Oh no, Red Hen!
I don't want a new house.
I'd just like to move this house
to the bottom of the hill.

**Mr. Fig:** That will be hard to do.
Perhaps we could use our magic
hats, Mama.

**Narrator:** When the rain stopped, all the animals but Rabbit put on their magic hats.

**Rabbit:** I left my hat in the Figmobile.
I must get it.

**Owl:** Be careful, Rabbit!
It has rained hard outside.
The road should be very muddy by now.

**Narrator:** Rabbit is heard shouting for help.

**Mouse:** That's Rabbit shouting.
Look! He's sliding down the
muddy hill.
I'll get his hat from the
Figmobile.

**Narrator:** Mouse gets Rabbit's hat.
He helps Rabbit back to the house.
Everyone sees that Rabbit is fine.

**Mr. Fig:** I'm not happy that you slid
down the hill, Rabbit.
But you just gave me a good idea!
Perhaps we can slide Mama Fig's
house down the muddy hill.
Our magic hats will help us
push the house.

**Mouse:** All we need to do is give the house a little push. Our magic hats and the mud should do the hard work.

**Narrator:** So they all push the house.
The house starts to slide down the muddy hill.
At last the house stops at the bottom of the hill.

**Turtle:** We did it!
Rabbit gave Mr. Fig a good idea.
Our magic hats and the mud helped us!

104

**Mama Fig:** I'm so happy!
Now I can be with my friends.
Thank you, everyone!

**Mr. Fig:** Mama, I must get
the Figmobile now.
I have to take my friends
to their homes.

**Narrator:** Mr. Fig gets the
Figmobile.
He rides down to the
bottom of the hill.
His friends and Mama Fig
wait outside for him.

**Mr. Fig:** Good-bye, Mama.
I'm so glad we could help you.
Climb in, everyone.
We have to go now.

**Animals:** Good-bye, Mama Fig!

**Mama Fig:** Good-bye!
Thanks again for all your help.

**Narrator:** Mama Fig's laughter is
heard as the friends fly higher
into the sky.
Mama Fig is very happy.
The friends are happy, too!

1. How did Mr. Fig and his friends make Mama Fig happy?

2. Why didn't Mama Fig like living on top of the hill?

3. How did Mr. Fig get the idea to help Mama Fig move her house?

4. What in this story made you smile?

5. When did you first begin to know that Mr. Fig and his friends would make Mama Fig happy?

6. Why was it good that Mama Fig's friends came to her house?

# Main Idea

Look at the picture below.
Then read what Mouse and Rabbit
are saying about the picture.
Who is telling the main idea?

Hen has on a hat.

They are flying.

Rabbit is telling the main idea
of the picture.
Mouse is only telling about
a small part of the picture.

108

Now look at the other two pictures.
Tell which animal is saying
the main idea in each picture.

*Do you think this story about why rabbits have long ears is true? Why? Why not?*

# Why Rabbits Have Long Ears

*retold by Valery Carrick*

Long ago there was a rabbit who made friends with a sheep. The sheep and the rabbit played together.

They did everything together. The sheep and the rabbit were very good friends.

One day the sheep said,
"Let's build a house!"

"Yes!" said the rabbit.
"Let's build a house."

So they went into the forest to get
some logs to build a house.
The sheep saw a tall tree.

"I can push this tree down!"
said the sheep.

"You cannot!" said the rabbit.

"Oh, yes I can," said the sheep.
"I'll show you!"

111

The sheep took a long run.
He hit the tree with his head.
The tree crashed down!
"You did it!" said the rabbit.
"Now I know how to push
down a tree, too."

Soon they saw another tall tree.
"I bet I can make that tree
come crashing down!" said
the rabbit.

"You cannot!" said the sheep.

"Oh, yes I can," said the rabbit.
"I'll show you!"

The rabbit took a long run.
He hit the tree so hard that his
head went into his shoulders.
The tree did not come crashing down.

"Rabbit! Your head went into your
shoulders!" said the sheep.
"I will help you."

The sheep put the rabbit's short
ears into his mouth and started to pull.

He pulled as hard as he could.

"Stop! Stop pulling my short ears!" the rabbit shouted.

But the sheep went on pulling.
At last the rabbit's head came out of his shoulders.

"You just about pulled my ears out of my head!" said the rabbit.

"Look! Look what you did to my short ears.
Now they are very long."

"Yes, your ears are very long," laughed the sheep.

*So now you know why rabbits have long ears!*

1. Do you think this story about why rabbits have long ears is true? Why?

2. Why did the rabbit run into the tree?

3. How did the rabbit's head get down into his shoulders?

4. How did you feel when the sheep was pulling the rabbit's ears?

5. When did you first know why rabbits have long ears?

6. The rabbit said that he could push down a tree just like the sheep did. What did he find out?

# Listen, Rabbit

*by Aileen Fisher*

I saw him first
when the sun went down
in the summer sky
at the edge of town
where grass grew green
and the path grew brown.

I couldn't tell
what he was at all
when I saw him first,
sort of halfway small,
sort of halfway grown,
near a gray old stone
in the field, alone.

Then I saw his ears
standing rabbit tall!

My heart went thump!
And do you know why?
'Cause I hoped that maybe
as time went by
the rabbit and I
(if he felt like *me*)
could have each other
for company.

*You will smile as you read about the race between a rabbit and a frog.*
*Read to find out how this race is won.*

# The Race

*Adapted from a Mexican Folktale*

by Dan Storm

One day Ramona Rabbit and Flora Frog were talking together. Ramona was bragging about how fast she could run.

"I can run faster than all the animals in Mexico!" she bragged.

Flora Frog was tired of Ramona's bragging about how fast she could run.

"I will be happy to race with you," said Flora.

Ramona Rabbit laughed. "Let's have the race this very day.
I will race you from the hill to the river."

"Not yet," said Flora.
"I need some time to get ready for the race."

Ramona Rabbit thought that it would be very easy to win the race.

Ramona called to Flora, "Just let me know when you are ready."

Flora Frog thought for a long time. "How can I win the race?" Then she had an idea.

The next day Flora called all the frogs together.

She asked her friends to make a line in the tall grass.

The line of frogs went all the way to the river.

Each frog was just one jump away from the next frog.

Then Flora went to tell Ramona that she was ready for the race.

"Let the race begin!" shouted
Ramona.

Ramona laughed as she ran
down the hill.
She looked to see if Flora was
behind her.

Ramona did not see Flora anywhere.

Then she saw a frog jump in front of her.

"Oh, no!" shouted Ramona. "Flora is in front of me."

"*Ándale! Córrele! Flojo!*" shouted the frog.

"Hurry up! Run! You slowpoke!"

Ramona put back her long ears and ran faster.

Just then a frog jumped up in front of her.

"*Ándale! Córrele! Flojo!*" that frog shouted.

"Hurry up! Run! You slowpoke!"

Each time Ramona looked up she saw a frog in front of her.

Each time she thought the frog was Flora.

Ramona was running so fast that she could not stop.

She ran right into the river.

"You won, Flora," Ramona said as she climbed out of the river.

Ramona was very tired, very sad, and very wet.

"I don't know how you did it!"

I have never seen a frog that can run as fast as you!"

Flora Frog just laughed.

"There are many frogs that can run as fast as I can."

1. How was this race won?

2. Why did Flora call all her frog friends together?

3. What was Flora trying to teach Ramona?

4. What did you think when Ramona said that she could run faster than all the animals in Mexico?

5. What made you think that this story took place in Mexico?

6. Ramona was better at running but Flora won the race. Why did Flora win?

*Hippo paints a picture.*
*Why does he have a hard*
*time painting the picture?*

# Hippo Paints a Picture

*by Mike Thaler*

It was a pretty morning.
Hippo was in the river.
The sky was bright blue.
The sun was bright yellow.

"I think I will paint a
picture," he said.
He climbed out of the river
and went to town.

Hippo got some yellow, red, blue, and white paint.

He got a brush and a cap.

He put on his cap and walked back home.

Then he started to paint.

He painted all morning.

By lunchtime, he had painted the grass, the tree, the hill, the sky and the sun.

"After lunch I will paint the flowers.
Then my picture will be finished,"
said Hippo.

Hippo ran home to eat his lunch.
Then he ran back and painted
the flowers.

"There," he smiled.
"I am finished."

Snake came to see Hippo's picture.

"It does not look finished to
me," said Snake.
"You did not put in that cloud."

"It was not there this morning,"
said Hippo.

"Well, it is there now," said Snake.

"All right," said Hippo.
He put some white paint on his brush
and painted the cloud.

"Now it is finished," said Hippo.

"Not quite," said Snake.
"A robin just landed on that tree."

"All right, all right," said Hippo.
"I will put him in."

Hippo painted the robin.
"Now my painting is perfect,"
he said.

"Not quite," said Snake, moving next
to the tree.
"You did not paint me."

"Come back here, Snake!" shouted Hippo.

"No!" said Snake.

"Please come here!" begged Hippo.

"No!" said Snake.

Just then, Lion came by.

More animals came by and stood next to the tree.

"Do you need any help?" they asked.

Hippo looked at all the animals
standing next to the tree.
Then he looked at his painting.
"I give up," he said.

He tossed his brush into the air
and walked away.

134

"Why did Hippo give up?"
asked Lion.

"He was having a hard time
with his painting," said Snake.

"Let's look at it," said Elephant.

All the animals walked away
from the tree and went to look
at the painting.

They looked at the grass and the
flowers, the hill and the sky,
the sun and the cloud, the
tree and the robin.

"I do not know why Hippo
was having a hard time,"
said Elephant.

"His painting looks perfect
to me!"

1. Why did Hippo have a hard time with his painting?

2. What did Snake want Hippo to paint in the picture?

3. What made Hippo give up painting?

4. How did you feel when Hippo gave up on his painting?

5. When did you know that Hippo was mad at Snake?

6. Hippo liked his painting at first. Why didn't he like it at the end of the story?

*Alexander Calder's art makes
people feel happy.
Read to find out why.*

# Alexander Calder

*by Catherine M. Carroll*

Alexander Calder was a great artist.
Alexander started making things
when he was five.

He made little toys and games.
He painted many pictures.
Alexander's mother and father
were artists, too.

They were happy that their son
liked to make things.

Alexander Calder liked to watch
the way things moved.

He loved watching how the animals
moved at the circus.

He drew pictures of circus animals.

When Alexander Calder grew up,
he made a toy circus.

People from all over the world
saw Calder's toy circus.

Collection of Whitney Museum of American Art.

Calder loved the moving toys
in his circus.

He wanted to make more
things that moved.

So he made children's toys
with moving parts.

Children loved to play
with the toys that Calder made.

Calder liked making mobiles
best of all.

Mobiles have many parts that move.
Some of his mobiles are very little.
Some are very big.

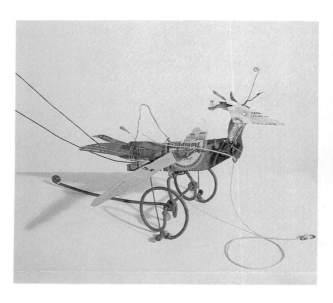

Calder liked to paint pictures, too.

He liked to use the colors red,
yellow, and blue in his pictures.

He liked these colors best of all.

Collection of Whitney Museum of American Art.

Alexander Calder was a very happy man.

He loved making things.

He said that his work was his play.

He thought that art should be happy.

He wanted his art to make people feel happy, too.

People laugh and smile when they see Calder's art.

1. Why does Alexander Calder's art make people feel happy?

2. Who is Alexander Calder?

3. Name some things that Alexander Calder made.

4. What do you like best about Calder's art?

5. How do you know that Calder was an artist for a long time?

6. Alexander Calder is happy when he is working. What do people do when they look at his art?

# Thinking About "Smiles"

You have read about people and animals who have helped others.

You have read about some animals who played funny tricks on their friends.

How did some friends help each other?

How did some friends play funny tricks?

Why does Alexander Calder's art make people feel happy?

The people and animals in the stories were happy when they helped others to smile.

Which stories made you smile?

1. How did some people and animals make others smile?

2. How are Flora Frog and Snake the same?

3. How are Hippo and Alexander Calder the same?

4. Which stories that you read could not be true? Why?
Which story is true? Why?

5. Do you think "Smiles" is a good name for this unit? Why?

# Long Ago

In "Long Ago" you will read about things that happened many years ago.

A grandfather tells how some things happen a little at a time.

You will learn about some very old and very big trees.

You will find out about a special present that a grandfather gave his son many years ago.

As you read, look for things that happened long ago.

Look for things that happened just a little at a time.

# Read on Your Own

**Red Fox and His Canoe** *by Nathaniel Benchley. Harper.* An Indian boy leaves home in his new canoe. He meets many forest animals and comes back with a small canoe.

**A Year of Birds** *by Ashley Wolff. Dodd, Mead.* Ellie and her family share a year with some birds.

**A Tree Is Nice** *by Janice May Udry. Harper.* A tree is nice to hang a swing on. It's also nice to rest under. This book tells many reasons why a tree is nice.

**Humphrey's Bear** *by Jan Wahl. Holt.* Humphrey loves an old toy bear that was once his dad's.

**Pumpkin, Pumpkin** *by Jeanne Titherington. Greenwillow.* Jamie plants a pumpkin seed. In the fall Jamie cuts the pumpkin and saves the seeds to plant.

**Days with Frog and Toad** *by Arnold Lobel. Harper.* In this book, you will find the story "The Kite," along with more Frog and Toad stories.

**If the Dinosaurs Came Back** *by Bernard Most. Harcourt Brace Jovanovich.* A boy tells what might happen if the dinosaurs came back.

**Grasshopper on the Road** *by Arnold Lobel. Harper.* A grasshopper meets some odd creatures along a road.

*In this story, a little boy learns many things from his grandpa. What does the little boy learn?*

# A Little at a Time

*by David A. Adler*

"How did that tree get to be so tall, Grandpa?" I asked.
"How did it get so tall?"

"When it started, it was just a seed. Then the seed grew and grew. It only grew a little at a time," Grandpa said.

"Why am I so small?" I asked.

"I used to be small like you,"
said Grandpa.
"You'll grow.
You will not grow as tall
as that tree.
You'll grow the way I grew,
a little at a time."

"How did this town get to be so big?

Were the buildings here always this tall, Grandpa?" I asked.

"All the buildings here used to be small.

As more room was needed, the small buildings were taken down.

Then these tall buildings were put up on the same land.

A town like this gets big, a little at a time," Grandpa said.

"Grandpa," I asked, "why is
this street so dirty?
  Was it always like this?"

"Many people drop things,"
Grandpa told me.
  "Each person may drop only a little.
  This street became dirty, just a little
at a time."

"Look at all these steps, Grandpa.
See how fast I can get to the top!"
I said.

"If you run to the top, I'll be
left back here.
Walk the way I walk, a little
at a time," Grandpa said.

"Grandpa, what is this?" I asked.

"These are dinosaur bones.
It took a long time to put the dinosaur bones together.
People dug up the bones and cleaned them.
Then they had to learn where each bone fit.
It was hard work," said Grandpa.

"I know how they did it, Grandpa," I said.
"They did it, a little at a time!"

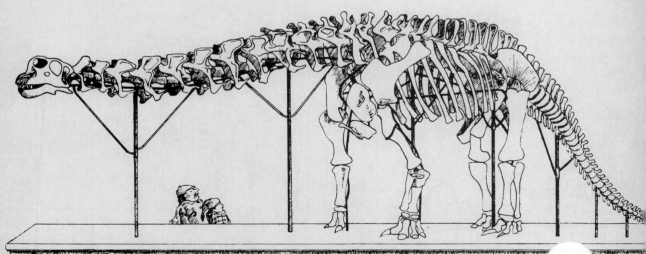

"How did you get to know so much, Grandpa?" I asked.

"I'm just like you!
I ask many questions.
Little by little I have learned a lot.
As long as I keep asking, I'll keep learning, a little at a time.
Now it's time to start going home," said Grandpa.

"How did it get to be so late, Grandpa?" I asked.

"You know the answer to that!" Grandpa said.
"The day went by, a little at a time."

1. What did the little boy learn from his grandfather?

2. How do many things happen in the world?

3. Name some other things that happen a little at a time.

4. What did you think when the little boy asked, "Why am I so small?"

5. When did you know that the little boy was telling this story?

6. Is it right to say the world is always changing? Why?

*Long ago, the giant sequoia trees were just little seeds. Find out what is happening to these trees today.*

# The Giant Trees

*by Emily J. Knowles*

The sequoia trees are very special trees.

They are very tall trees.

They are very old trees.

They are very pretty trees.

They are the biggest living things!

How did they grow to be so big?

The sequoia trees started
as little seeds many years ago.
   The little seeds grew into
tiny plants.
   The tiny plants grew into trees.
   Each year the trees grew
bigger and bigger.
   After many, many years,
they became giant trees.

5 years    25 years    75 years    1,000 years    3,000 years

People were surprised when they
first saw these giant trees in
California.

They knew that they could get a
lot of wood from these giant trees.

They wanted to use this wood
to make things.

Many sequoia trees were cut down.

160

After the trees were cut down,
their stumps were left in the forest.
One day, some people found the
stump of a giant sequoia tree.
This stump was so big that many
people could get on it at one time.

Soon, too many of the trees had been cut down.

People wanted to stop this.

They knew that the sequoias took a long time to grow.

They wanted to save the trees.

Now the sequoia trees are being saved.

Each year, many people come to California to see these giant trees.

They know that the sequoias are very old and very special trees.

The sequoias are the biggest trees in the world.

They got to be this way, a little at a time.

1. What is happening to the giant sequoia trees today?

2. Why were the sequoia trees being cut down?

3. Why do people go to California to see the sequoia trees each year?

4. What did you think when you saw the picture on page 158?

5. What in the story told you that it took the sequoia trees a long time to grow?

6. Why is it a good idea to save the giant sequoia trees?

163

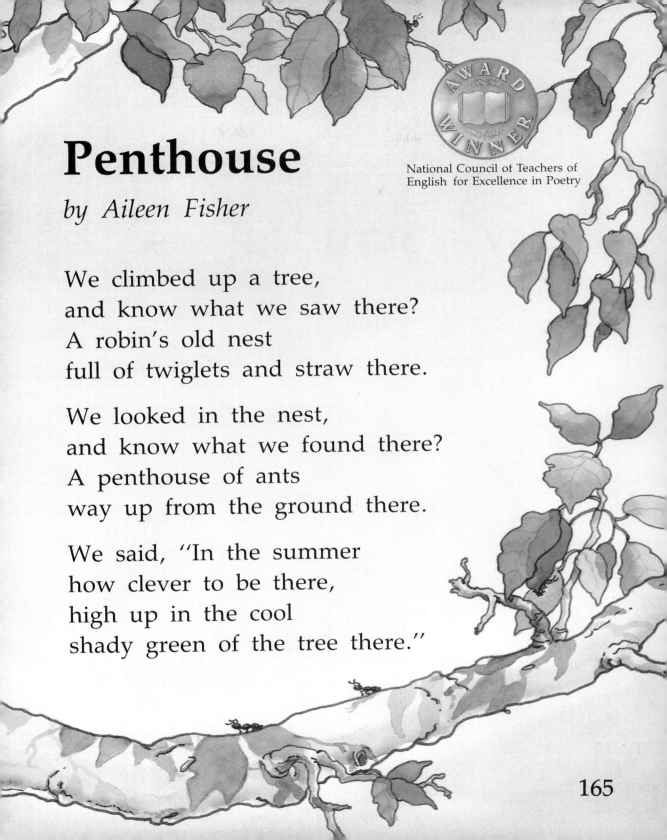

# Penthouse

*by Aileen Fisher*

National Council of Teachers of
English for Excellence in Poetry

We climbed up a tree,
and know what we saw there?
A robin's old nest
full of twiglets and straw there.

We looked in the nest,
and know what we found there?
A penthouse of ants
way up from the ground there.

We said, "In the summer
how clever to be there,
high up in the cool
shady green of the tree there."

*Daisy finds something that her grandpa gave her father long ago. What surprise will Daisy's father give to her? Why?*

# Daisy's Surprise

*by Dolly Cebulash*

As Daisy was helping her father clean, she found a tiny canoe.

"Look at this canoe, Dad," she said. "It looks just like your big canoe."

Daisy's father laughed.

"So it does," he said, "but this canoe is much smaller.

Your grandpa gave me this canoe when I was a little boy."

166

"Why did Grandpa give you this toy canoe?" asked Daisy.

"Your grandpa took me fishing in his canoe many years ago," said her father.
"We didn't catch any fish that day.
But we had a good time.
The very next day, he made me this smaller canoe out of wood.
He said that when I looked at the canoe, it would make me think of that day."

"Does it make you think of that day, Dad?" asked Daisy.

167

"Oh, yes," said Daisy's father.
"I'd like to take you fishing sometime just as Grandpa used to take me.
Would you like to go fishing with me, Daisy?"

"Oh yes!" said Daisy.
"I hope that we can go soon!"

The very next morning, Daisy's father put the canoe on the truck.
Daisy helped her father make lunch and put the fishing things in the truck.
Then Daisy and her father waved good-bye to her mother as they rode away in the truck.
Before long, they were at a pond.

Daisy got out of the truck and looked
at the pond.

She looked at the tall trees near
the pond.

She heard the wind in the trees.

"What a pretty place," said Daisy.

"Yes, it's very nice here," said Daisy's
father as he took the fishing things out
of the truck.

Daisy and her father got into the canoe and went out on the pond.

They sat in the canoe for a long time, waiting to catch some fish.

Sometimes they talked.

Sometimes they just watched and waited.

"This is like the day you went fishing with Grandpa and didn't catch any fish!" Daisy laughed.

Just then a fish jumped up out of the water.

"You've got a fish," Daisy's father said.
He helped Daisy pull it in.
Daisy looked at the fish.
It looked sad.
Daisy's father got a long string.
He tied the fish to the string.
Then he gave the end of the string
to Daisy.

"Now you can pick up the fish," her
father said.

Daisy held the end of the string and
looked at the fish.
The fish was trying to get away.
"I want to let it go," Daisy said.

"I thought you wanted to catch a fish," said Daisy's father.

"I did," said Daisy, "but I wanted this day to be like the day you had with Grandpa."

"I see," her father said as he helped her take the fish off the string.

They dropped the fish back into the water and watched it swim away.

Soon it was time to go home.

Daisy and her father laughed about the fish as they rode home.

Daisy went right to sleep that night. It had been a nice day!

The next day, when Daisy's father came home from work, he had a surprise for her.

It was tied with string.

"Open it," he said.

Before Daisy opened it, she said, "I think I know what it is.

It's a small canoe."

Her father just laughed.

When Daisy opened the surprise, she laughed, too.

173

"Oh, Dad," said Daisy, "it's not a canoe.

It's a toy fish, just like the fish I got at the pond."

"When you look at this fish, I hope you will think of our day," said her father.

"Thank you, Dad!" Daisy said as she hugged her father.

"This will always make me think of our day at the pond!"

1. What surprise did Daisy's father give her? Why?

2. Why did Daisy think the surprise from her father was a small canoe?

3. What happened when Daisy and her father went fishing?

4. How did you feel when Daisy opened the surprise?

5. When did you first begin to know that Daisy's surprise was not a canoe?

6. Why were the toy fish and the canoe both special?

*American Indians made canoes many years ago.*
*How did they make them?*

# A Better Way

*by Marie L. Smith*

Long ago, many American Indians lived near water.

They wanted to travel on the water. They wanted to travel fast.

They also wanted to carry things with them when they traveled.

The American Indians tried to find a way to do these things.

The American Indians saw logs floating on the water.

They sat on the floating logs.

They used long sticks to help them move the logs in the water.

Sometimes it was hard to stay on the logs.

It was also hard to carry things on the logs.

They soon found that using floating logs was not the best way to travel.

The American Indians tried to find a better way.

Then the American Indians
tied logs together to make rafts.

They found that they could carry
things on the rafts.

They could also fish from them.

But the rafts did not go very fast.

Sometimes the things on the rafts
got wet.

They soon found that using rafts
was not the best way to travel.

The American Indians tried again
to find a better way.

Now the American Indians
had another idea.

First, they looked for a log from a
big tree.

Next, they made a small fire
on top of that log.

Soon they put out the fire.

Then the Indians chipped the
burned wood out of the log.

They put the log in water and
sat inside it.

The log moved fast, and the things
they took with them did not get wet.

They had found a better way
to travel.

The American Indians
had made a canoe.

Today, canoes are still used.

Some people travel in canoes, and some people use them just for fun.

Many people are glad that the American Indians found a better way.

1. How did the American Indians make canoes long ago?

2. How did the American Indians travel on water before they had canoes?

3. Why didn't the American Indians want to keep using the floating logs and rafts?

4. The American Indians found many ways to travel on water. Which one do you like best?

5. What clues do you have that "A Better Way" is a good name for this story?

6. How are canoes still used today?

# Study Skills

# Follow Directions

## Make a Paper Canoe

You just read two stories about canoes.

Now you can make a canoe out of paper.

You will need to follow directions carefully to make your paper canoe.

Make a
Paper Canoe

182

To follow directions, here are some things that you will need to do.

1. Get all the things you will need.
2. Read each step of the directions carefully.
3. Start with step 1 and then follow each step after that.

*Things you will need:*

scissors          paste          crayons

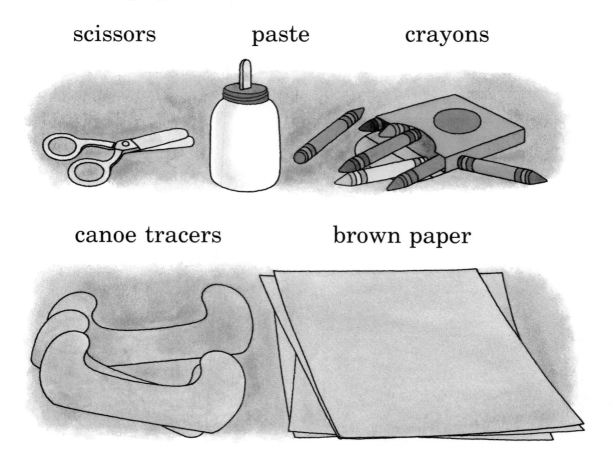

canoe tracers                    brown paper

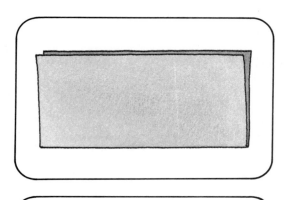

Now follow these directions carefully.

1. Fold the brown paper.

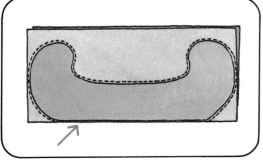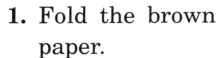

2. Put the canoe tracer on the fold and trace it.

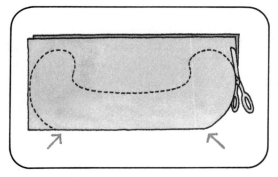

3. Cut out the canoe. Do not cut on the fold.

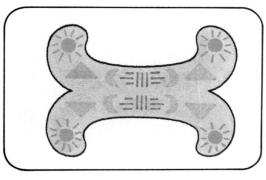

4. Open the canoe. Then draw pictures on the canoe and color them.

184

**5.** Turn the canoe over and put a little paste on the ends.

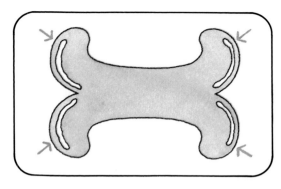

**6.** Put the pasted ends together.

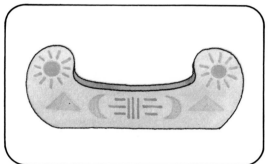

When you are finished, your canoe may look like one of these.

*Sometimes there are better ways of doing things.*
*How do Frog and Toad find a better way to fly a kite?*

# The Kite

*story and pictures by Arnold Lobel*

Frog and Toad went out to fly a kite.

They went to a large meadow where the wind was strong.

"Our kite will fly up and up," said Frog.

"It will fly all the way up to the top of the sky."

"Toad," said Frog,
"I will hold the ball of string.
You hold the kite and run."

Toad ran across the meadow.

He ran as fast as his short legs could carry him.

The kite went up in the air.

It fell to the ground with a bump.

Toad heard laughter.

Three robins were sitting in a bush.

"That kite will not fly," said
the robins.
"You may as well give up."

Toad ran back to Frog.
"Frog," said Toad, "this
kite will not fly.
I give up."

"We must make a second try,"
said Frog.
"Wave the kite over your head.
Perhaps that will make it fly."

Toad ran back across the meadow.
He waved the kite over his head.

The kite went up in the air
and then fell down with a thud.

"What a joke!" said the robins.
"That kite will never get off
the ground."

Toad ran back to Frog.
"This kite is a joke," he said.
"It will never get off the ground."

"We have to make a third try,"
said Frog.
"Wave the kite over your head
and jump up and down.
Perhaps that will make it fly."

Toad ran across the meadow
again.

He waved the kite over
his head.

He jumped up and down.

The kite went up in the air
and crashed down into the grass.

"That kite is junk," said
the robins.

"Throw it away and go home."

Toad ran back to Frog.
"This kite is junk," he said.
"I think we should
throw it away and go home."

"Toad," said Frog,
"we need one more try.
Wave the kite over your head.
Jump up and down and shout
*Up, kite, up.*"

Toad ran across the meadow.
He waved the kite over his head.
He jumped up and down.
He shouted, "Up, kite, up!"

The kite flew into the air.
It climbed higher and higher.

"We did it!" cried Toad.

"Yes," said Frog.
"If a running try
did not work,
and a running and waving try
did not work,
and a running, waving,
and jumping try
did not work,
I knew that
a running, waving, jumping,
and shouting try
just had to work!"

The robins flew out of
the bush.

But they could not fly
as high as the kite.

Frog and Toad sat
and watched their kite.

It seemed to be flying
way up at the top of the sky.

1. How did Frog and Toad find a better way to fly a kite?

2. What happened the first three times Frog and Toad tried to fly the kite?

3. What is the real reason Frog and Toad could get the kite to fly?

4. How did you feel when the robins told Toad that the kite would never get off the ground?

5. When in the story did you know that the kite would fly?

6. If Toad had given up on the first try, how would the story be different?

# Thinking About "Long Ago"

Many of the stories you have read were about things that happened a long time ago.

You read about a little boy who learned many things from his grandfather.

You learned how the giant sequoia trees took many years to grow.

You read about people and animals who found better ways of doing things.

Why did Daisy's father and grandfather give special presents?

What are some things that happened a little at a time?

Which stories told about things that happened long ago?

1. What would Grandpa in "A Little at a Time" tell the boy about the sequoia trees?

2. How did the American Indians of long ago help Daisy's father?

3. Who are the two grandfathers that you read about?
   What did each grandfather do?

4. How are the stories "The Giant Trees," "A Better Way," and "The Kite" the same?

5. Why do you think this unit was named "Long Ago"?

# Word Helper

"Word Helper" develops readiness for dictionary skills and provides students with a reference for words they may wish to use in their writing. Example sentences for all the new words in this book are provided. Illustrated sentences are followed by ■.

## Aa

| | |
|---|---|
| **across** | Tim ran **across** the playground. |
| **airplane** | She flew the **airplane.** |
| **also** | We **also** want to go for a swim. |
| **answer** | Robert knows the right **answer.** |
| **any** | Does the zoo have **any** seals? |
| **art** | The **art** was pretty. |

**artist**     An **artist** may paint a picture. ■

# Bb

**been**     I have **been** to the zoo before.

**before**     Let's eat lunch **before** we go.

**began**     This morning it **began** to rain.

**behind**     The dog is sitting **behind** him.

**below**     We saw birds **below** the clouds. ■

**biggest**     Ramona found the **biggest** frog.

| | |
|---|---|
| **bill** | A canary has a small **bill.** |
| **both** | **Both** of us like to ride bikes. |
| **bottom** | The turtle swam to the **bottom.** |
| **brown** | Mother has a **brown** horse. |
| **build** | The boys will **build** a plane. |
| **buildings** | The **buildings** are quite small. |
| **burned** | The old tree **burned** down. |
|  **bush** | The **bush** has red flowers. ■ |

# Cc

**canoe**      Two of us can go in the **canoe.** ■

**care**      I take good **care** of my toys.

**careful**      Be **careful** on the playground.

**carefully**      She **carefully** drew a dinosaur.

**carrier**      I want to be a mail **carrier.**

**carry**      We can **carry** the canoe.

**cave**      The bear stayed in the **cave.**

**cheer**      **Cheer** up, or I'll be sad, too.

**children**    The **children** played together.

**circus**    We had fun at the **circus.** ■

**cleaned**    Rick **cleaned** under the bed.

**count**    I'll **count** everyone here.

**crashed**    A plate fell down and **crashed.**

# Dd

**deep**    He looked into the **deep** hole.

**dinosaur**    This **dinosaur** lived long ago.

**dirty**     Please clean the **dirty** plates.

**dolphin**   We saw a **dolphin** do tricks. ■

**drew**      He **drew** pictures of animals.

# Ee

**ears**      People have small **ears.**

**easy**      We think it's **easy** to swim.

**eat**       Is it time to **eat** lunch? ■

**everyone**  **Everyone** is ready for school.

**eyes**      Rosa and I have brown **eyes.**

# Ff

**fancy**        Paco has a **fancy** toy bear.

**fast**        The horse went **fast.**

**faster**        Ramona began to skip **faster.**

**feed**        Nina helped **feed** her canary.

**finished**        He **finished** reading the story.

**fire**        We made a small **fire.**

**forest**        A **forest** has many trees in it. ∎

**found**        I **found** the toy that I lost.

**four**        All **four** friends had fun.

| | |
|---|---|
| **front** | Amy is sitting in **front** of me. |
| **funny** | The clown did a **funny** trick. |

# Gg

| | |
|---|---|
| **gave** | Eddie **gave** Grandpa a present. |
| **giant** | An elephant is a **giant** animal. ∎ |
| **good-bye** | Is it time to say **good-bye?** |
| **ground** | Flowers grow in the **ground.** |

# Hh

**happen**     What is going to **happen** today?

**hard**     A rock is very **hard.**

**head**     He has a hat on his **head.**

**heard**     We **heard** the boys singing.

**high**     Emily climbed the **high** hill.

**higher**     Can the plane go any **higher?**

**hook**     I put my hat on the **hook.** ■

# Ii

**I'd**     **I'd** been looking for that toy!

**idea**     You had a good **idea.**

# Jj

**junk**     He made a mobile out of **junk.** ■

# Kk

**key**     May I see the map **key,** too?

**knew**     We **knew** the way to the river.

# Ll

**large**  A **large** bear begged for food.

**last**  **Last** year I couldn't read.

**laughed**  We **laughed** at the clown. ■

**laughter**  **Laughter** says we are happy.

**learn**  He will **learn** to swim soon.

**left**  She **left** her bike at home.

# Mm

**mail**  All of us like to get **mail**.

**mailbox**  I was looking for a **mailbox.**

**main**  The **main** road in town is wide.

**map**  He drew a **map** of the town. ■

**marine park**  We saw otters at a **marine park.**

**meadow**  Flowers grew in the **meadow.**

**mobiles**  The air makes **mobiles** move.

**more**  I would like **more** for lunch.

**morning**  The sun comes up each **morning.** ■

**mouth**  A shark has a very big **mouth.**

| | |
|---|---|
| **move** | Pam can **move** that big rock. |
| **much** | Papa is **much** bigger than Todd. |
| **muddy** | It is **muddy** near the pond. |

# Nn

| | |
|---|---|
| **never** | I have **never** seen a pelican. |
| **newspaper** | I read the **newspaper** today. ■ |
| **nothing** | There was **nothing** in the box. |

# Oo

**old**  Emily likes her **old** toys best.

**otters**  People came to see the **otters.** ∎

**outside**  Wait for me **outside** the store.

# Pp

**paper**  Flora drew a picture on **paper.**

**part**  I read **part** of the newspaper.

**paw**  My cat put her **paw** on the ball.

**peacock**      We like to feed the **peacock.** ■

**pelican**      The **pelican** is a sea bird.

**perfect**      This is a **perfect** day for a walk.

**perhaps**      **Perhaps** we'll catch some fish.

**plants**      Many **plants** grew by the house. ■

**playground**      We ran around the **playground.**

**post office**      Mail this at the **post office.**

**pretty**      Those flowers are very **pretty.**

**prevent**      We must **prevent** forest fires.

**pulled**     The horse **pulled** a big cart.

# Qq

**questions**     You can ask your **questions.** ∎

**quite**     We are not **quite** ready to go.

# Rr

**race**     The boys want to have a **race.**

**rafts**     We rode **rafts** down the river.

| | |
|---|---|
| **raindrops** | Big **raindrops** fell on us. |
| **ranger** | A **ranger** works in the forest. ■ |
| **read** | I **read** a story this afternoon. |
| **ready** | The boys are **ready** to go home. |
| **right** | That is the **right** answer. |
| **river** | I like to walk by the **river.** |
| **robin** | The **robin** will eat the worm. |
| **room** | The horse has **room** to run. |

# Ss

| | |
|---|---|
| **sea** | Fish live in the **sea.** |

| | |
|---|---|
| **second** | Lee ran in the **second** race. |
| **sent** | We **sent** a present to Grandma. |
| **sentences** | These **sentences** make a story. |
| **sequoia** | A **sequoia** can grow very tall. ■ |
| **shark** | A **shark** is a big animal. |
| **short** | This story is very **short.** |
| **should** | Jan **should** help us clean. |
| **shoulders** | He sat on the man's **shoulders.** |
| **signed** | Rick **signed** his letter to Tim. |
| **small** | Nina has a **small,** toy rabbit. |

| | |
|---|---|
| **smaller** | My bike is **smaller** than yours. |
| **smelled** | I thought lunch **smelled** good. |
| **smoke** | The fire made a lot of **smoke.** |
| **sorted** | We **sorted** the paints by color. |
| **starfish** | **Starfish** live in the sea. ■ |
| **stars** | Amy is looking at the **stars.** |
| **started** | I **started** to paint my picture. |
| **stomach** | A canary has a small **stomach.** |
| **stood** | Margie **stood** near the door. |

| | |
|---|---|
| **story** | Dad told me a monster **story.** |
| **string** | The box is tied with a **string.** |
| **stump** | A robin sat on the tree **stump.** ■ |
| **swam** | Emily **swam** over to the rock. |
| **swim** | We like to **swim** in the pond. |

# Tt

| | |
|---|---|
| **taken** | I had **taken** my bike home. |
| **talk** | I like to **talk** to my friend. |

| | |
|---|---|
| **we're** | **We're** painting pictures. |
| **which** | **Which** story did you like best? |
| **woman** | Someday Rosa will be a **woman.** |
| **won** | Today, she **won** all the games. |
| **wood** | The door is made of **wood.** ■ |
| **world** | I want to go around the **world.** |
| **worm** | The **worm** went into the hole. |

# Yy

| | |
|---|---|
| **year** | This **year** my brother will go to school. ■ |

**you're**    I hope **you're** glad to be here.

# Zz

**ZIP code**   Do you know your **ZIP code?** ■

# Word List

The following words are introduced in this book. Each is listed beside the number of the page on which it first appears. The words printed in color are words that students can decode independently.

## A New Friend
*(6–13)*

| 6 | found |
|---|---|
| | playground |
| | I'd |
| | told |
| | much |
| 8 | post office |
| | an |
| | ad |
| | newspaper |
| | small |
| | brown |
| | lick |
| | lot |
| 9 | by |
| | bed |
| 10 | woman |
| 11 | we're |
| | we'd |
| 12 | miss |
| | you'll |
| | you're |

## Smokey the Bear
*(14–21)*

| 14 | last |
|---|---|
| | story |
| | read |
| | forest |
| | ranger |
| 15 | smelled |
| 16 | smoke |
| | fire |
| 17 | ground |
| | hot |
| | burned |
| | paw |
| 18 | any |
| 19 | prevent |

## Little Bear and Emily
*(24–31)*

| 24 | high |
|---|---|
| | wide |
| | world |
| 25 | river |
| | sea |
| 26 | began |
| | worm |
| | talk |
| 27 | treetop |
| | together |
| 28 | good-bye |
| 30 | laughed |

## The Surprise Letters
*(32–41)*

| 32 | someone |
|---|---|
| | sent |
| 33 | best |
| 34 | funny |
| | still |
| | signed |
| | drew |
| 35 | their |
| 36 | rode |
| 37 | thought |
| 39 | grass |
| | smiled |

## Maps
*(42–43)*

| 42 | map |
|---|---|
| | key |

## Amy Mails a Letter
*(44–49)*

| 44 | mailbox |
|---|---|
| | mail |
| | carrier |

took
45 sorted
size
ZIP code
46 truck
airplane

## Owly
*(56–65)*

56 started
questions
stars
count
57 three
four
morning
more
closing
eyes
59 higher
60 waves
62 deep
63 gave

## Predict Outcomes
*(68–69)*

68 happen
raindrops
69 water
swim

## Ottie and the Star
*(70–75)*

70 learn
71 swam

shark
fast
cave
outside
72 dolphin
under
73 starfish
74 waved

## At a Marine Park
*(78–83)*

78 marine park
jobs
otters
cleaned
79 feed
plants
eat
mouths
its
stomach
80 care
net
dropped
81 train
82 clap

## Pelly and Peak
*(84–91)*

84 peacock
land
pelican
fine
fan
nothing
85 fancy
cheer

86 log
never
careful
87 hook
bite
88 pulled
woke
89 bill
sand
easy
90 both
inside

## Mama Fig's House
*(98–107)*

99 laughter
heard
everyone
100 before
hard
101 should
bottom
perhaps
move
102 left
muddy
103 he's
sliding
slid
idea
104 mud

## Main Idea
*(108–109)*

108 main
below
only

226

K
L
M
N